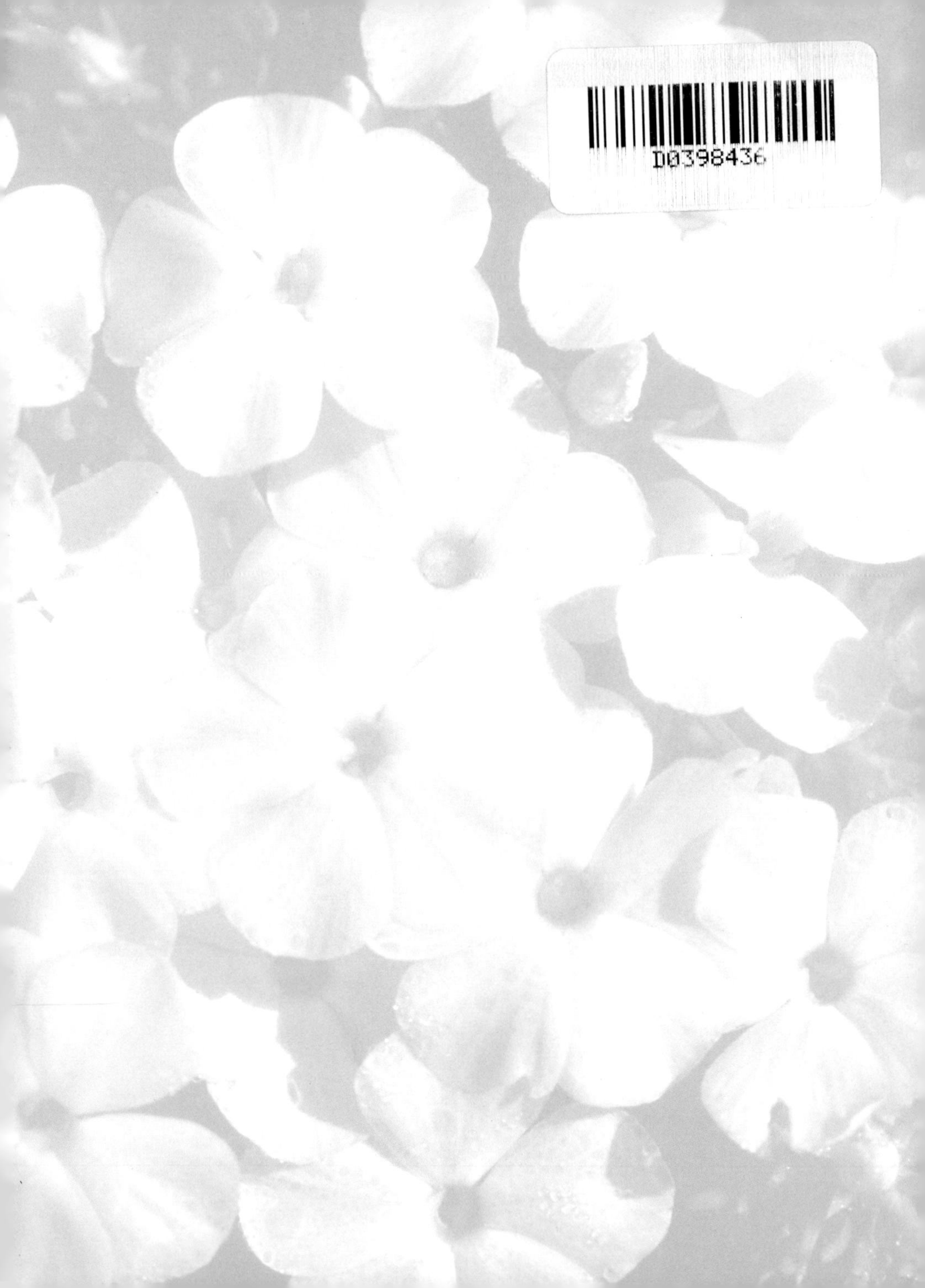

_To_

From

HIS PEACE WILL

KEEP YOUR _thoughts_

Philippians 4:7

Journal: His peace will keep your *thoughts*
Copyright © 2000 Garborg's
Published by Garborg's
P. O. Box 20132, Bloomington, MN 55420

Design by Franke Design

ISBN 1-58375-654-X

Journal

God's peace will keep your thoughts
and your hearts quiet and at rest.

PHILIPPIANS 4:7 TLB

Quiet Waters

"HE LEADS ME BESIDE QUIET WATERS."
PSALM 23:3

A living, loving God
can and does
make His presence felt,
can and does
speak to us in the
silence of our hearts,
can and does
warm and caress us till
we no longer doubt that
He is near,
that He is here.

Joy is not happiness so much as gladness; it is the ecstasy of eternity in a soul that has made peace with God.

The world stands out *on either side*

No wider

than the heart is wide;

Above the world

is stretched the sky,—

No higher

than the soul is high.

The heart can push the sea and land
Farther away
on either hand;
The soul can
split the sky in two,
And let the face of God
shine *through.*

EDNA ST. VINCENT MILLAY

There is nothing but God's grace. We walk upon it; we breathe it; we live and die by it; it makes the nails and axles of the universe.

ROBERT LOUIS STEVENSON

What *happens* when we
live God's way?
He brings **gifts**
into our lives,
much the same way

that fruit *appears* in an orchard—

things like affection for others,

exuberance about life,

serenity.

GALATIANS 5:22 MSG

*Something deep in all of
us yearns for God's beauty,
and we can find it no
matter where we are.*

SUE MONK KIDD

Listen to your life.
See it for the **fathomless**

mystery that it is.

In the *boredom and pain* of it

no less than in the

excitement and **gladness:**

touch, *taste,* smell your way

to the **holy** and *hidden* heart of it

because in the last analysis

all moments are *key* moments

and **life** itself is *grace.*

FREDERICK BUECHNER

God *guides us,* despite our uncertainties and our **vagueness,** even through our f a i l i n g s a n d m i s t a k e s....
He *leads us* step by **step,** from event to event.
Only afterwards, a s w e l o o k b a c k over the way we have come and *r e c o n s i d e r* certain important **moments** in our lives

in the light of all that has followed them...

do we experience the feeling

of having been led without knowing it,

the feeling that God has

mysteriously *guided us.*

PAUL TOURNIER

For God is, indeed, a wonderful Father who longs to pour out His mercy upon us, and whose majesty is so great that He can transform us from deep within.

TERESA OF AVILA

God waits for us
in the inner sanctuary
of the soul.
He welcomes
us there.

RICHARD J. FOSTER

*God bless you and
utterly satisfy your
heart...with Himself.*

AMY CARMICHAEL

Let the **beloved** of the Lord
rest secure in him,
for he **shields** him
all day long,
and the *one*

the Lord **loves**

rests

between his shoulders.

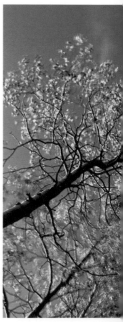

DEUTERONOMY 33:12 NIV

*God's love is like a river springing
up in the Divine Substance and
flowing endlessly through His
creation, filling all things with life
and goodness and strength.*

THOMAS MERTON

No, it is *not yours* to open
buds into **blossom**....
He who can o p e n the bud
does it so simply.
He gives it a glance and the life sap
stirs through its veins.

At His breath the flower
spreads its wings
and *flutters* in the wind.
Colors flash out like heart longing,
the perfume betrays a *sweet* secret.
He who can o p e n the bud
does it so simply.

TAGORE

*Whoever walks toward
God one step, God runs
toward him two.*

JEWISH PROVERB

The thought of You
stirs us so deeply
that we cannot be content
unless we praise You,
because You have made us
for Yourself and *our hearts*
find no peace until
they rest in You.

AUGUSTINE

*We have been in God's
thought from all eternity,
and in His creative love,
His attention never leaves us.*

MICHAEL QUOIST

The **ordinary** acts
we practice **every** day
at **home** are of more
importance to the soul
than their *s i m p l i c i t y*
might suggest.

THOMAS MOORE

*What lies behind us and what
lies before us are tiny matters
compared to what lies within us.*

RALPH WALDO EMERSON

God's peace...

is far more *w o n d e r f u l* than

the human mind can

understand.

His peace will *keep your thoughts*

and your hearts *quiet*

and at rest.

PHILIPPIANS 4:7 TLB

God still draws near to us in the ordinary, commonplace, everyday experiences and places.... He comes in surprising ways.

HENRY GARIEPY

The God who created,

names, and numbers the stars

in the heavens also

numbers the hairs of my head....

He pays attention to

very big things and

to very small ones.

What matters to me matters to Him,

and that changes my life.

ELISABETH ELLIOT

That is God's call to us—
simply to be people who are
content to live close to Him
and to renew the kind of life
in which the closeness is felt
and experienced.

THOMAS MERTON

It is not objective proof

of God's existence

that we want but the

experience of God's presence.

That is the miracle

we are really after, and that

is also, I think, the miracle

that we really get.

FREDERICK BUECHNER

*Inside myself is a place where
I live all alone, and that is
where you renew your springs
that never dry up.*

PEARL S. BUCK

May the Lord bless
and protect you;
may the Lord's face
radiate with joy
because of you;
may He be gracious to you,
show you His favor, and
give you His peace.

NUMBERS 6:24-26 TLB

God knows the rhythm of my spirit and knows my heart thoughts. He is as close as breathing.

It is an *extraordinary* and beautiful thing that God, in creation... works with the *beauty* of matter; the reality of things;

the discoveries of the *senses*,
all **five** of them;
so that we, in turn,
may hear the grass growing;
see a face **springing** to life
in **love** and *laughter*....
The **offerings** of creation...
our *glimpses* of **truth**.

MADELEINE L'ENGLE

*He makes me lie down in green
pastures, he leads me beside
quiet waters, he restores my soul.*

PSALM 23:2-3 NIV

We must **drink deeply**
from the very Source
the **deep calm** and *peace of interior*
quietude and **refreshment** of God,
allowing the **pure** water
of **divine grace** to
flow plentifully and **unceasingly**
from the Source itself.

MOTHER TERESA

When you draw close to God,
God will draw close to you.

JAMES 4:8 TLB

In comparison with this
big world, the human heart is
only a *small* thing.
Though the world is so large,
it is utterly unable to s a t i s f y
this *tiny heart.*
Our ever growing soul
and its capacities can be s a t i s f i e d
only in the infinite God.
As water is r e s t l e s s until
it reaches its level, so the soul
has no peace until it r e s t s in God.

SADHU SUNDAR SINGH

God is the sunshine that warms
us, the rain that melts the frost
and waters the young plants.
The presence of God is a climate
of strong and bracing love,
always there.

JOAN ARNOLD

The *wonder* of our Lord
is that He is so accessible to us
in the common things of our lives:
the cup of water...
breaking of the bread...
welcoming children into our arms...
fellowship over a meal...
giving thanks.
A simple attitude of *caring, listening,*
and lovingly telling the *truth.*

NANCIE CARMICHAEL

*There is a calmness to a life
lived in gratitude, a quiet joy.*

RALPH H. BLUM

O Lord, you have
examined my heart
and know everything about me....
You both precede and
follow me, and place
your *hand of blessing*
on my head.

PSALM 139:1,5 TLB

Love has its source in God,
for love is the very essence
of His being.

KAY ARTHUR

An **infinite** God can
give *all* of Himself to each
of His children.

He does not d i s t r i b u t e Himself
that **each may** have a part,
but to each one He **gives**
all of Himself
as **fully** as if
there were no **others.**

A. W. TOZER

*Be beautiful inside, in your
hearts, with the lasting charm
of a gentle and quiet spirit
which is so precious to God.*

1 PETER 3:4 TLB

Still **round** the
corner there may $wait$,
a *new* road,
or a *secret*
gate.

J. R. R. TOLKIEN